HUMOROUS TALES OF

Mulla Nasruddin

A SET OF 5 BOOKS

1

CLASSIC LITERATURE FOR CHILDREN

1. THE BRAINY NASRUDDIN
2. THE MULLA RESCUES THE MOON
3. THE MULLA ATTENDS A FEAST
4. WON'T THE POCKET FEEL THIRSTY?
5. OH! THE MULLA'S HANDWRITING
6. A BAD OMEN FOR THE MULLA
7. THE LAST FEAST
8. THE MULLA SITS BACKWARDS ON THE DONKEY

AUTHOR
YOGESH JOSHI

ADAPTATION
ASMITA BHATT

ILLUSTRATIONS
SIDDHARTHA MUKHERJEE

navNeet®

F 4601   **PRICE : RS. 45.00 (BOOK 1)**

1. THE BRAINY NASRUDDIN

The following incident occurred
many years ago
when Mulla Nasruddin was very young.

One day,
Nasruddin reached late to school.
The teacher
was quite annoyed with him.
Taking the rod in his hand,
he said angrily,
"Nasruddin,
why are you so late?"

Making a pitiable face,
little Nasruddin
said meekly,
"It wasn't my fault, sir.
Hardly had I left home
for school
when there arose
a violent storm,
and suddenly it began to rain.
It was raining very heavily...
and a strong wind began to blow...
I soon realized
the wind was blowing
from the opposite direction.
The gusts of wind
were so strong
that for every step I took forward,
I was forced back two steps.
I would take a step forward...
and be pushed back two steps...
One forward...
two back..."

The teacher was perplexed.
He began to play
with the rod in his hand –
a sign that he was thinking seriously
about something.
He then asked Nasruddin,
"If you took one step forward...
only to be pushed back two steps,
how did you reach school?"

Little Nasruddin said,
"Ah! I used my brains, you see.
Instead of walking
towards school,
I started walking
towards home.
In this way,
I would take one step
towards home...
and get pushed two steps
towards school.
And so here I am...
Better late than never!"

2. THE MULLA RESCUES THE MOON

It was a full moon night.
Mulla Nasruddin
was walking towards his village.
His long, quick stride revealed his great hurry.
Soon the Mulla reached
the outskirts of his village.
"Oh! Thank God,"
he mumbled, feeling rather relieved.
On the outskirts of the village,
there was an old well.
The Mulla thought,
"Umm... Let me see
how much water there is in this well."
The Mulla walked up to the well
and peeped inside.
"Oh my God!"
he exclaimed.
"The moon has fallen
into the well!
The water in the well
must be very cold.
What if the moon freezes!
Or she might even melt in the water...

6

Let me pull the moon out
with the help of a long rope.
I will then toss her like a ball.
I will toss her very high...
and z...o...o...m...
She will reach there...
high up in the sky."

Thinking thus,
the Mulla went home
and brought a long rope.
He tied it like a lasso
and flung it
into the well.
He then shouted,
"Hey moon!
Don't be frightened.
Hold the rope tightly.
I will pull the rope out..."

Unfortunately,
the rope got hooked
somewhere deep inside the well.
The Mulla tried very hard...
He struggled to pull the rope out,
but it was all in vain.
The Mulla thought,
"I think the moon is very heavy.
I must pull the rope with all my might."
The Mulla rested his right foot
firmly on the edge of the wall
and shook the rope vigorously.
Then with all his might,
he began to pull the rope.
Suddenly, the rope was detached
from where it was hooked in the well.
The Mulla fell down
with a loud thud.
He fell flat on his back.
And his head banged hard
against the ground.
The Mulla was dazed.
For a few moments,
he felt woozy;
and he soon fainted.

After some time,
when the Mulla
regained his consciousness,
he opened his eyes.
And what did he see?
There was a big, bright moon
high up in the sky!

The Mulla was beside himself with joy.
He said to himself,
"I have injured myself.
But it doesn't really matter now.
I have succeeded
in rescuing the moon.
I have pulled her out
from the well
and sent her back
into the sky!
And that is why
she is looking at me
with a sweet smile
on her face!"

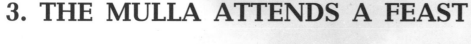

3. THE MULLA ATTENDS A FEAST

One day,
a rich man of the village
held a grand feast.

Mulla Nasruddin was also invited
for the feast.
Feeling rather pleased at this,
the Mulla left
for the rich man's house.
His lively gait
reflected his excitement.
As he was walking down the road,
he said to himself,
"Ah! A feast at the *amir's* house!
There will be a variety of
tasty dishes to eat.
It has been a long time
since I last attended a lavish feast
and savoured some new dishes.
I'm going to eat
till my stomach
is more than full!"

With a view to relishing a lot of tasty dishes,
the Mulla had fasted the previous day.
Soon he reached near the *amir's* house.
From a distance,
he saw the grand pandal.
The Mulla started walking quickly
towards the venue.

When the Mulla reached the gate
of the pandal,
he was stopped by a guard.
"Why are you going in?"
said the guard in a stern voice.
"Come after the feast is over."

The Mulla was taken aback!
He realized
that the guard was staring
at his filthy clothes,
dishevelled hair,
and long, dusty beard.
When the guard saw the Mulla,
he said to himself,
"I'm sure this man is a beggar."

Without saying a word,
the Mulla returned home.
He washed his hands and face...
combed his hair...
and even cleaned his beard.
He then wore his new silk pyjamas,
and a long brocade coat.
He wore a silk turban
adorned with a beautiful tassel.
He liberally sprayed
the costliest perfume
on his new clothes,
and looked at himself in the mirror.
"Ooh! I do look like a *nawab*!"
he said,
feeling rather confident.
The Mulla again left
for the *amir's* house.
But this time,
his gait reflected
his confidence and self-esteem.
Showing off his rich style,
he walked down the road
like a *nawab*...
and soon reached the pandal.

And this time,
the guard saluted him politely.
The *amir* himself
came to receive the Mulla.
They greeted each other
with several bows
and courteous salutations.
The *amir* made the Mulla
sit beside him for the feast.
A variety of dishes
was served in silver plates.
All the invitees
began to request one another
to start eating.
"After you…"
said one
"No… no…
after you…"
insisted the other.
These courtesies went on
for quite some time.
At last,
the *amir* started eating.
But the Mulla
still would not start eating.

Instead of enjoying the feast,
the Mulla removed his turban
and put it in front of the silver plate
filled with tasty dishes.
He then said,
"O turban!
Eat these dishes...
They are for you only."
Holding the hem of his brocade coat
in front of the silver plate,
the Mulla said,
"O my rich brocade coat!
Eat these dishes...
They are for you only."

The *amir* was astonished
at the strange behaviour
of the Mulla.
"Has this man gone wacky?"
he wondered.
However,
he asked the Mulla,
"What is the matter?
Why are you doing all this?"

The Mulla said,
"When I first came here,
I had worn soiled clothes.
So the guard did not allow me
to enter the pandal.
But when I came back
wearing rich, impressive clothes,
I was given great respect and honour!
This means…
It wasn't I,
but my rich clothes
that were invited for the feast.
And so I am asking my clothes
to enjoy the feast."
The *amir* burst out laughing.
He said,
"The guard has made a mistake.
He failed to recognize you.
The Mulla,
whether he is in simple clothes…
or in rich clothes,
will always remain the Mulla."
Having said this,
the *amir* put a sweet
into the Mulla's mouth.

15

4. WON'T THE POCKET FEEL THIRSTY?

One day,
Mulla Nasruddin went to attend
the wedding of a rich man.
There was still some time
for the lavish lunch.
And therefore,
all the guests were being served
sweets and dry fruits as snacks.
The guests were sitting in groups
and enjoying themselves.
They were chatting with one another
and relishing the snacks.

The Mulla thought,
"If I eat such heavy snacks now,
I won't be able to enjoy the lunch."
Thinking thus,
the Mulla took
only some dry fruits.
As he was about to put
an almond into his mouth,
he saw that
one of the guests
had filled his plate
with plenty of dry fruits.
The guest was looking around
to make sure
no one was watching him.
He then quietly put
a handful of dry fruits
into his pocket!
The Mulla was amazed.
He shook his head in disbelief.
Just then,
once again,
the guest looked around cautiously
and put another handful of dry fruits
into his pocket!

17

The Mulla got up quietly
and brought a jug
filled with water.
Holding the jug in his hands,
he walked towards the guest
and quietly stood behind him.
He then pulled the guest's pocket,
and began to pour water into it.

The guest
flew into a towering rage.
He screamed,
"What is all this nonsense?!
Have you gone mad?
Look what you have done!
My new coat!
It is all soaked!"

Now all the guests present there
turned their attention
to the commotion.

The Mulla said loudly,
"Your pocket was very hungry.
And so it ate up
plenty of dry fruits.
Now after eating so much,
won't the pocket feel thirsty?
And that is why I gave water
to your pocket..."

And the guest was dumbfounded.

5. OH! THE MULLA'S HANDWRITING

One day,
Mulla Nasruddin
sat in his favourite rocking chair.
He put on his glasses
and began to read something.

Just then,
one of his relatives came
to meet him.

He said to the Mulla,
"My son lives in Baghdad.
I have to call him back
as soon as possible.
I want you to write
such a letter
that the moment he reads it,
he will leave Baghdad
and return home immediately."

"But I have no plans
to go to Baghdad now,"
said the Mulla.
His relative said,
"And I am not suggesting
any such thing.
I am certainly not asking you
to personally go to Baghdad
and fetch my son here."

The Mulla ignored his relative
and continued to read.
But the relative was persistent.
He said,
"You must write a letter
to my son
and ask him to return at once.
I am sure
when my son reads the letter,
he will come home immediately."

The Mulla said,
"I don't mind writing the letter.
But then I will have to
personally take it to Baghdad."

21

The relative assured him,
"Believe me,
you need not go to Baghdad.
All you have to do is
write a letter for me.
I will send it with someone
who is going to Baghdad."
The Mulla looked at his relative
over the rim of the glasses,
which had slipped
a little down his nose.
He said,
"I know…
You will send the letter
with someone
who is going to Baghdad.
But then
who will read it?"

22

The relative said,
"Well, let me tell you...
My son is not an illiterate like me.
He can read and write."

The Mulla said,
"Oh, I didn't mean that.
I know
your son can read and write.
But the problem is..."

Before the Mulla could say further,
the relative said impatiently,
"Well, what's the problem?"

The Mulla said,
"The problem is...
my handwriting.
You see
my handwriting is so bad
that only I can read it.
And so I myself
will have to go to Baghdad
to read out the letter!"

23

6. A BAD OMEN FOR THE MULLA

One day,
the emperor was going on a hunting trip
along with his entourage.
Just then,
he saw Mulla Nasruddin
walking towards him.
When the emperor saw the Mulla,
he was very irritated.
His face reflected his great displeasure.
He barked,
"Did the Mulla
have to cross my path today?
What a bad omen this is!
Now I'm sure
this hunting trip
won't be a good one.
Punish the Mulla
with five lashes."

The Mulla bowed to the king
and greeted him politely.
He then requested the king,
"But Your Majesty,
you…"
Before the Mulla could say
anything further…
S…w…a…s…h.
S…w…a…s…h.
A guard began to lash him mercilessly.
"Oh… ouch… ouch…"
The Mulla cried with pain,
but no one cared for his screams.

The emperor
and his entourage
then went their way.

After some time,
they reached the forest.
On the banks of a lake
in that forest,
there stood a tall tree.
A *machan*
had already been built on it.
The emperor climbed up
on the *machan*.
The guards,
armed with bows and arrows,
and spears,
placed themselves
on the surrounding branches.
Everybody was on the alert.
They were looking all around,
eager to spot an animal.
But they didn't have to wait very long.
The emperor was lucky!
A huge tiger
came to drink water from the lake.

The emperor took aim and shot an arrow.
S...w...o...o...s...h.
The arrow pierced the tiger's chest.
Meanwhile, the guards also sent
a volley of arrows at the tiger.
The tiger fell down dead.
The emperor was delighted.
The next day,
when he went to the court,
he called the Mulla and said,
"Ah! Mulla Nasruddin...
You have proved to be
very lucky for me!
When I saw you yesterday,
it was such a good omen
that we didn't have to wait very long
to hunt a majestic tiger."
Stroking his long beard,
the Mulla said politely,
"But Your Majesty...
You were not so lucky for me!
When I saw you yesterday,
it was such a bad omen
that I got five lashes.
Have you thought about it?"

7. THE LAST FEAST

Mulla Nasruddin
was a proud owner
of a nice, fat sheep.
And his neighbours envied him
for possessing
such a fine and healthy sheep.
Some of them were even tempted
to own it.
So one day,
the Mulla's jealous
and greedy neighbours
got together
and hatched a plot
to kill the sheep.

According to the plan,
one day,
the neighbours
came to the Mulla.
One of them said,
"Mulla Nasruddin,
did you hear the prophecy?"

"What prophecy?"
asked the Mulla, innocently.
"O my God,"
exclaimed another neighbour.
"Look at this man...
Hasn't he heard anything?!
Dear Mulla,
do you know
tomorrow is Doomsday?
Tomorrow,
the whole world
will come to an end!"
The Mulla was stunned.
"What?!" he screamed.
"What are you saying?
That can't be true."
The third neighbour said,
"Tomorrow will be the last day
of the Earth's existence...
Not a single living being
will stay alive after tomorrow.
And so enjoy yourself now.
Eat what you like...
Drink what you like...
And fulfil your last wish."

The neighbours keenly watched
the changing expressions
on the Mulla's face.
"Ah!
He seems to have believed our story,"
they thought,
feeling quite pleased with themselves.
One of them said,
"Umm…
Doomsday…
Before we all die tomorrow,
let's have a grand feast."
Another neighbour said,
"Let's go to the banks of the river
for a lovely picnic.
We will cook something there
and enjoy a grand feast
in the cool breeze."
Yet another neighbour said,
"The Mulla's sheep
will also die tomorrow.
Then why not kill it today?"
"Oh, yes.
Why not?"
said the rest of them in unison.

30

"Yes, yes.
Why not?"
said the Mulla.
Now this was an unexpected reaction
from the Mulla,
who loved his sheep very much.
Well, what else could explain the fact
that he did not protest
against the idea of killing his sheep?
In this way,
the Mulla and his neighbours
got ready and left for the river-bank.
While the food was being prepared,
they enjoyed swimming in the river.
When the food was laid before them,
they began to eat it hurriedly.
While relishing the lavish feast,
the neighbours looked at one another.
There was a wicked smile
on their faces.
Each of them thought,
"Ah! We have fooled the Mulla.
We have killed his sheep
to enjoy this feast today."

All of them ate to their heart's content.
Their stomachs were so full
that they soon began to feel sleepy.
So they removed their coats,
hung them on a branch of a tree
and lay down under the tree
to take a quick nap.
The cool breeze of the river
was blowing gently...

And soon…

Z...z...z...   Z...z...z...   Z...z...z...

All of them began to snore.

After making sure

that all his neighbours were fast asleep,

the Mulla got up quietly.

He took all the coats,

dumped them together,

and set fire to them.

When the sleeping neighbours

got the smell of something burning,

they woke up with a start.

And what did they see?

Their coats were ablaze!

"Hey Mulla!

What have you done?"

they shouted.

The Mulla said calmly,

"Tomorrow,

the whole world

will come to an end!

Then what is the use of these coats?

So I used the coats to light a little fire

to keep us warm...

for the last time, I suppose..."

8. THE MULLA SITS BACKWARDS ON THE DONKEY

One day,
the Mulla accidentally overheard
his pupils' conversation.
They were discussing among themselves,
"If we do this,
what will people say?
And if we do that,
how will we look?"
So the Mulla said to himself,
"The people can say what they like.
We should always do what we think is right."
But he didn't want to say anything
directly to his pupils.
He thought,
"If I give them any advice,
they might not listen to me.
They will never overcome the fear
of what people might say.
So instead of advising them,
let me think of a plan
to teach them what I want to
by setting a good example."

After thinking for a few moments,
the Mulla came up with a plan.

He called one of his pupils
and said,
"Bring my donkey here.
And tell all the pupils
that they have to come with me.
And yes…
They should come with me
in whatever clothes
they are wearing now.
None should wait to change his clothes."

The pupil brought the donkey,
and the Mulla sat on it.
But he sat backwards on the donkey!
His face was in the direction
of the donkey's tail;
while his back was towards
the donkey's face!
Seeing this,
one of the pupils asked the Mulla,
"Sir, why are you sitting backwards
on the donkey?"

The Mulla said,
"I will answer your question
when the time comes.
But right now…
all of you must come with me
without asking any questions."
The Mulla then said to his donkey,
"O my wise pupil!
We now have to take a stroll
through the streets
of the village.
So come on…
march quickly…"
In this way,
the Mulla sat backwards
on his donkey
and the strange procession
began to roam through the streets
of the village.
The procession
was led by the Mulla,
who was sitting backwards
on the donkey.
He was followed by his pupils,
dressed in old, filthy clothes!

36

Everyone who saw this weird procession
remarked,
"The Mulla is a fool...
and his pupils are greater fools!"

Soon a big crowd of people
began to follow the procession.
As they walked along,
they shouted,
"The Mulla is a fool...
and his pupils are greater fools!"

In no time,
the number of people
following the procession
began to increase rapidly.
Everybody laughed at the Mulla.
Some shouted the 'slogan',
"The Mulla is a fool...
and his pupils are greater fools!"
While some others
poked fun at the Mulla.
Little children enjoyed
running after the procession
and watching the amusing scenes.

The Mulla was the least bothered.
But one of his pupils
could not bear the ridicule.
He said to the Mulla,
"Sir, the people are mocking at us.
And yet you don't seem to care!"
The Mulla said,
"No, I don't care.
This mockery does not bother me.
As you can all see...
I am sitting on this donkey
and enjoying the ride..."
But then another pupil got so irritated
that he said,
"You are free to sit on a donkey.
But for God's sake...
Why are you sitting backwards on it?"
The Mulla said calmly,
"Let people say whatever they want to.
They are free do whatever they like.
Now suppose I sit straight on the donkey,
and you walk in front of me...
Well, you would be walking
with your back towards me...
And that is an insult to the teacher.

38

And now suppose...
you walk behind me...
Well, I can't see your faces then...
And that is what I don't like.
Right now I am sitting backwards
on the donkey.
So I am able to look at you
and even talk to you easily!
And there is nothing wrong in it, is there?
I really don't understand
why all of you are so upset about this.
Now let me help you
get rid of your fears and grievances.
I will now say loudly,
'The Mulla is a fool!'.
And you have to say,
'His pupils are greater fools!'"
The Mulla then said loudly,
"The Mulla is a fool!"
"His pupils are greater fools!"
shouted his pupils, in a chorus.
This continued for quite some time.
Now the mob was no longer interested
in following the procession.
Soon the mob dispersed.

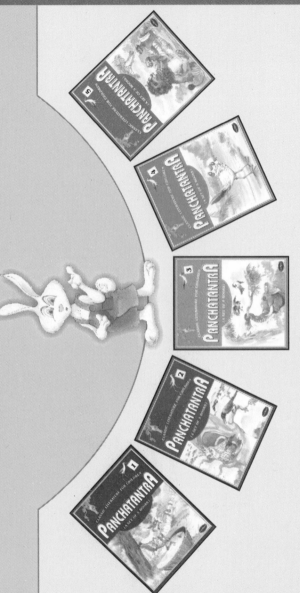

CLASSIC LITERATURE FOR CHILDREN

PANCHATANTRA
(A set of five books)

Panchatantra, originating in ancient folklore, still holds a unique place in world literature. The stories from the Panchatantra help readers to study and understand behavioural patterns in man. These stories are a source of knowledge and worldly wisdom. They inspire young minds to develop a strong moral fibre.

The stories in these books are written in simple and well-structured language and illustrated with beautiful pictures.

Also available in Gujarati, Hindi, Marathi & Bengali.

NavNeet®

Where knowledge is wealth ™